THE COMPLETE ORGAN PLAYER

(BOOK THREE)

BY KENNETH BAKER

CONTENTS

SONGS

Published by Wise Publications
London/New York/Sydney

**Teacher & Student's Guide to the
Complete Organ Player**
This excellent guide written by
Kenneth Baker contains valuable notes
to the nine books of the Complete Organ
Player Course. It is available from
Music Sales Limited, 78 Newman Street, London W1P 3LA.
For your free copy, please send 25p in stamps
to cover postage and handling.

Exclusive distributors: Music Sales Limited, 78 Newman Street, London W1P 3LA.

ISBN 0.86001.383.9
AM 19456

Cover design: Howard Brown

Printed in England by West Central Printing Co. Ltd., London and Suffolk

REGISTRATION TABLE (3)
(For All Organs)

GENERAL ELECTRONIC ORGANS

(1) Upper: Flute 8′ 4′ 2′
Lower: Flute 8′ String 8′
Pedal: 8′
Vibrato: On (Leslie: Trem.)

(2) Upper: Oboe (Reed) 8′
Lower: Flute 8′ 4′
Pedal: 8′
Vibrato: On (Leslie: Trem.)

(3) Upper: String 8′ 4′
Lower: Flute 8′ 4′
Pedal: 8′
Vibrato: On (Leslie: Trem.)

(4) Upper: Trumpet 8′ Trombone 8′
Lower: Flute 8′ 4′
Pedal: 16′ + 8′
Vibrato: Off (Leslie: Chorale)

(5) Upper: Flute 8′ 4′ String 8′ Trumpet 8′
Lower: Flute 8′ 4′ Diapason 8′
Pedal: 16′ + 8′
Vibrato: On (Leslie: Trem.)

(6) Upper: Flute 8′ 4′ Clarinet 8′
Lower: Flute 8′ String 8′ (or Diapason 8′)
Pedal: 8′
Vibrato: Off (Leslie: Chorale)

(7) Upper: Flute 16′ 8′ 4′ Clarinet 8′ Reed 8′
Lower: Flute 8′ 4′ Diapason 8′
Pedal: 16′ + 8′
Vibrato: On (Leslie: Trem.)

(8) Upper: Flute 16′ 8′ 4′ Trumpet 8′ String 8′
Lower: Flute 8′ 4′ Diapason 8′
Pedal: 16′ + 8′
Vibrato: On (Leslie: Trem.)

DRAWBAR ORGANS

(1) Upper: 00 7605 000
Lower: (00)5443 211(0)
Pedal: 4 - (2)
Vibrato: On (Leslie: Trem.)

(2) Upper: 00 4675 300
Lower: (00)3433 211(0)
Pedal: 4 - (2)
Vibrato: On (Leslie: Trem.)

(3) Upper: 00 5675 542
Lower: (00)6442 000
Pedal: 4 - (2)
Vibrato: On: (Leslie: Trem.)

(4) Upper: 00 7888 643
Lower: (00)8761 210(0)
Pedal: 5 - (3)
Vibrato: Off (Leslie: Chorale)

(5) Upper: 00 7766 336
Lower: (00)6754 221(0)
Pedal: 5 - (3)
Vibrato: On (Leslie: Trem.)

(6) Upper: 30 8783 003
Lower: (00)5654 432(0)
Pedal: 4 - (2)
Vibrato: Off (Leslie: Chorale)

(7) Upper: 44 8644 567
Lower: (00)5655 432(0)
Pedal: 5 - (3)
Vibrato: On (Leslie: Trem.)

(8) Upper: 73 6668 568
Lower: (00)6655 444(0)
Pedal: 5 - (4)
Vibrato: On (Leslie: Trem.)

Basic Rhythm:-

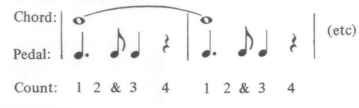

Chord:

Pedal:

Count: 1 2 & 3   4   1 2 & 3   4

This pedal rhythm is sometimes called the **BAION** bass.

Registration Nº ②
Suggested Drum Rhythm:- **Rock**

Green Green Grass Of Home

Words and Music by Curly Putman

The old home town looks the same as I step down from the
house is still stand-ing tho' the paint is cracked and

train____ and there to meet me is my ma - ma and pa - pa____
dry____ and there's that old oak tree that I used to play on____

Down the road I look and there runs Ma - ry,
Down the lane I walk with my sweet Ma - ry,

Hair of gold and
Hair of gold and

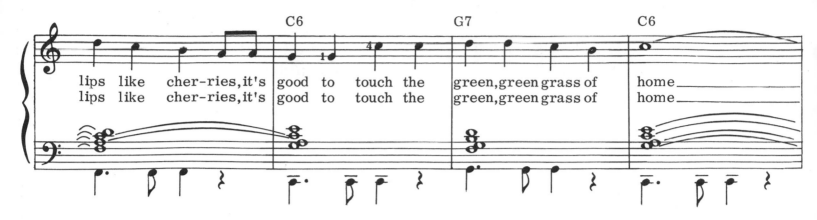

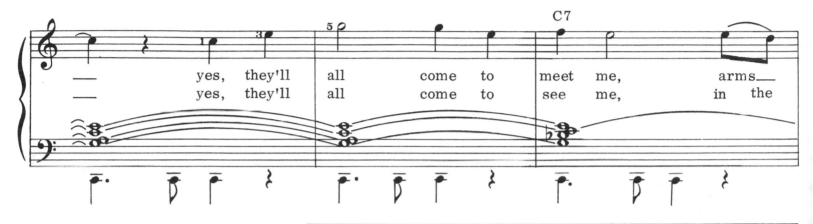

5

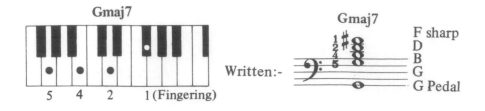

For All We Know

Registration Nº ④
Suggested Drum Rhythm:- **Bossa Nova**

Words by Billy Towne. Music by Fred Karlin. English lyric by S. K. Russell

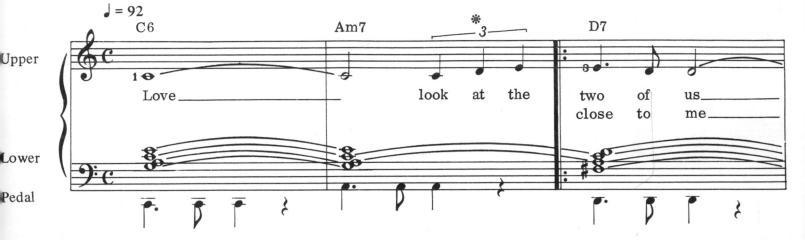

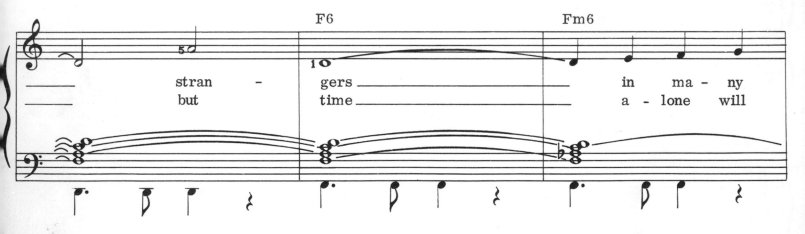

* CROTCHET (QUARTER NOTE) TRIPLET. 3 Crotchets played in the time of 2.

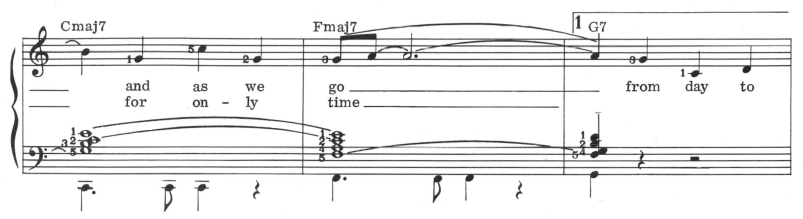

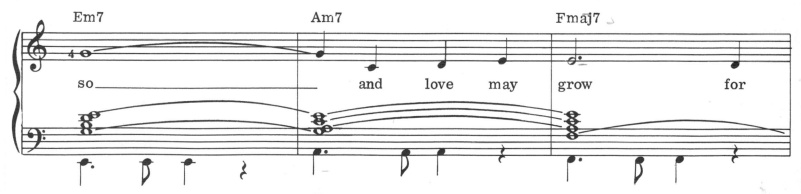

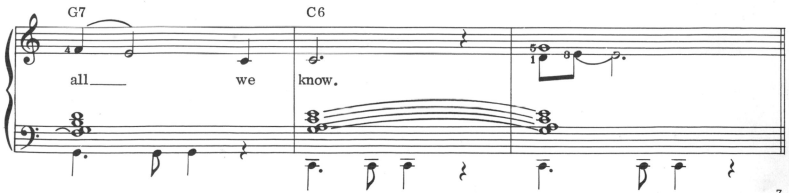

CHORDS ON DIFFERENT PEDAL NOTES

Up to now the pedal notes played have been the same as the letter names of the chords (with C6 a C pedal, with F6 an F pedal, and so on). This will continue to be the usual case. Now and again, however, we shall use a different note in the pedals to good effect.

In the next piece we play an F♯° (E♭°) chord, WITH A PEDAL D, written:- F♯° (on D).

NEW CHORDS

The Fool On The Hill

Words and Music by John Lennon and Paul McCartney

Registration N° ⑥
Suggested Drum Rhythm:- Rock

♩ = 92

Day af – ter day___ a – lone on a hill___

The man with the fool – ish grin is keep – ing

per – fect – ly still___ But no – bod – y wants to

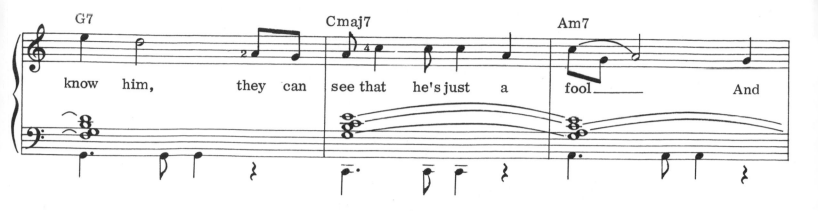

know him, they can see that he's just a fool____ And

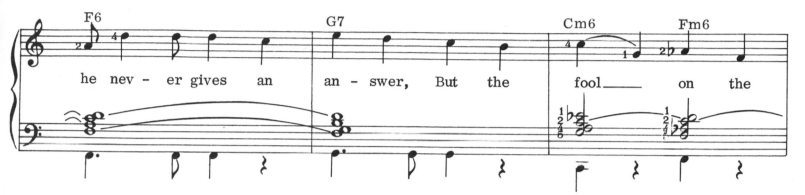

he nev - er gives an an - swer, But the fool____ on the

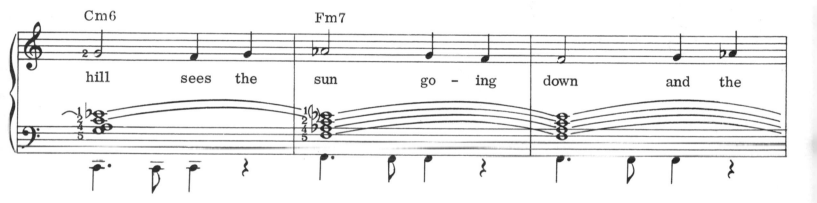

hill sees the sun go - ing down and the

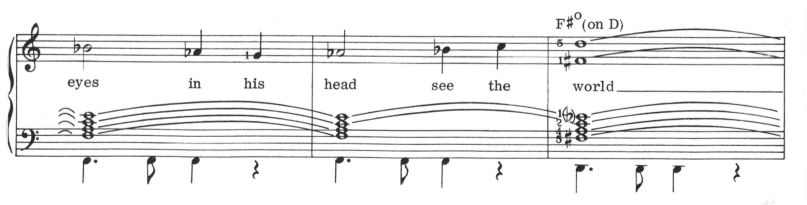

eyes in his head see the world____

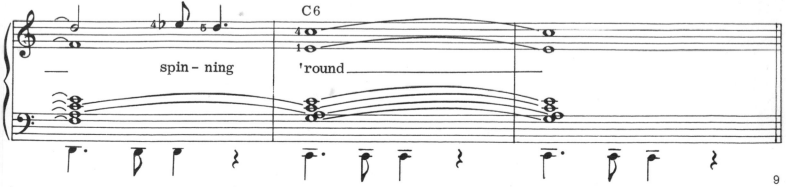

____ spin - ning 'round____

AUGMENTED CHORDS

There are four basic types of chord:- MAJOR (e.g. C), MINOR (e.g. Cm), DIMINISHED (e.g.Eb°), and AUGMENTED. We have already met the first three. The fourth type: AUGMENTED (usually written: +) is often best left as a three note chord.

NEW CHORD

And I Love You So
Words and Music by Don McClean

Registration No ③
Suggested Drum Rhythm:- **Bossa Nova**

NEW LOW INVERSION

As was the case with E7 it is sometimes more convenient to play Gm7 in a lower inversion. You will recognise this chord as being the same as Bb6, but of course the pedal note is different.

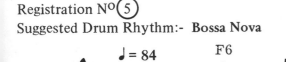

My Way

French lyric by Gilles Thibaut. English lyric by Paul Anka. Music by Claude Francois and Jacques Revaux

Registration Nᵒ⑤
Suggested Drum Rhythm:- **Bossa Nova**

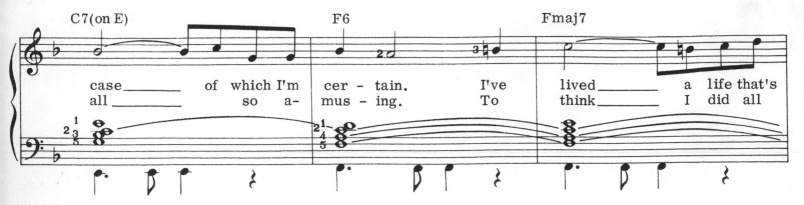

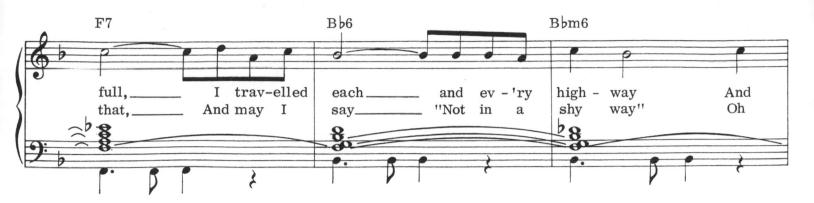

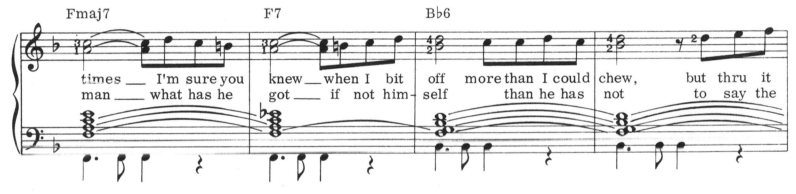

Basic Rhythm:-   Chord:
Pedal:

(etc)

The melody must be kept smooth (joined) whilst the left hand clips its chords short, giving a nice "lift" to the rhythm.

ACCIACCATURA (Bars 1,2,3, and 4):-

A type of ornament quite often used in Jazz. The Acciaccatura note (G Sharp) is played just before, but almost simultaneously with, the main note (A). It is then released, leaving the main note (A) singing.

SLUR (Bars 15/16, Bars 31/32)

A curved line connecting two (different) notes. (In this case a note and a chord). The second of the two notes is to be made less important than the first. On the organ this is usually done by making the second of the two notes staccato (detached).

Dance Of The Cuckoos (Laurel & Hardy Theme)

by Marvin Hatley

Registration Nº ④
Suggested Drum Rhythm:- Waltz

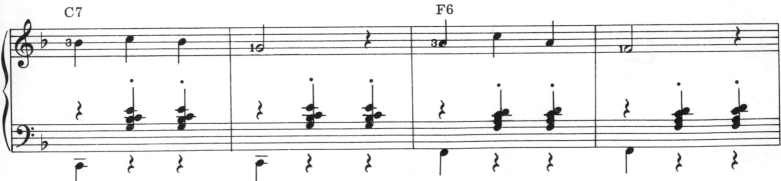

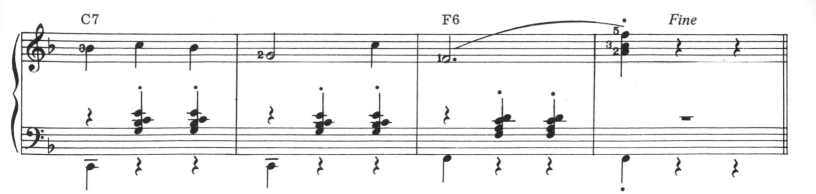

C7   F6   *Fine*

Vib: On
Leslie: Trem.

C7

F6

Vib: Off
Leslie: Chorale

C7   F6

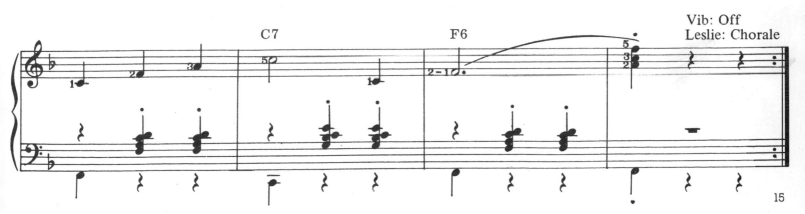

15

Cruising Down The River

Words and Music by Eily Beadell & Nell Tollerton

Registration N⁰ ⑦
Suggested Drum Rhythm:- Waltz

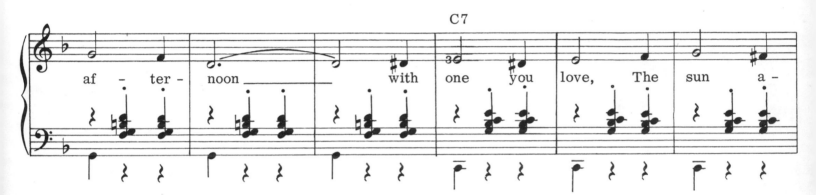

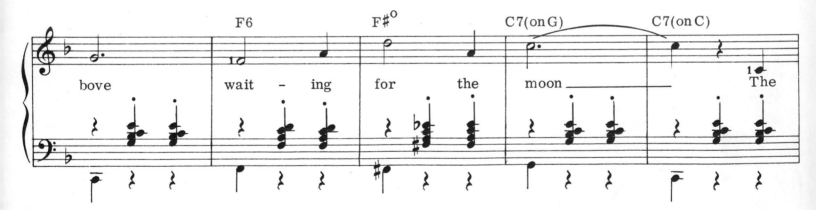

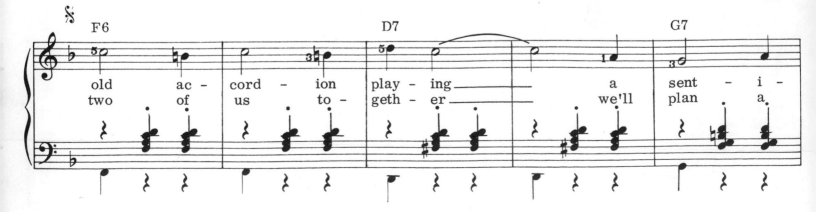

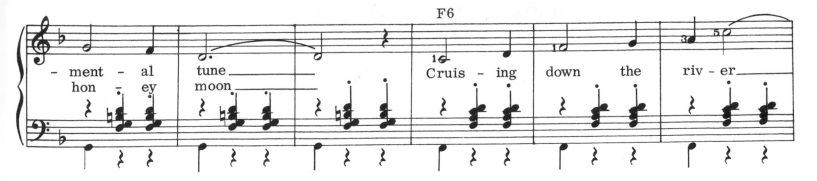

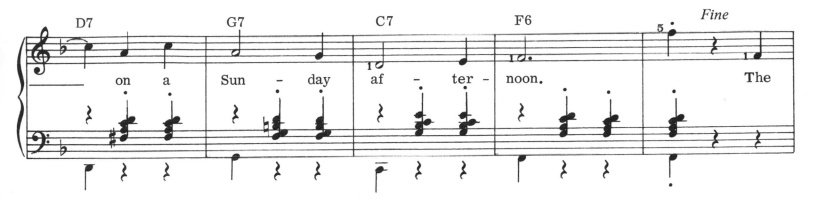

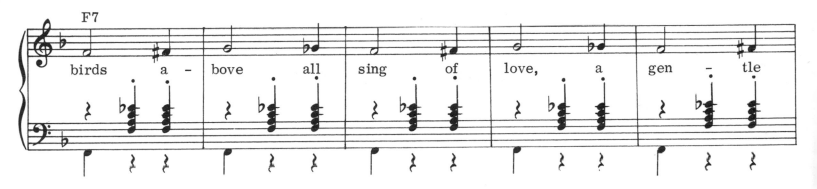

*DAL SEGNO AL FINE: "from the Sign 𝄋 to FINE." i.e. make a repeat.

17

Upstairs, Downstairs (Theme From)
By Alexander Faris

Registration Nº ⑧
Suggested Drum Rhythm:- Waltz

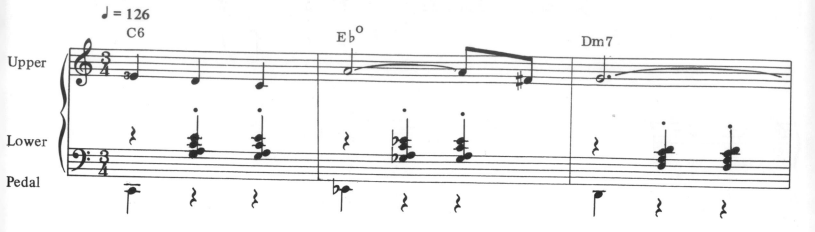

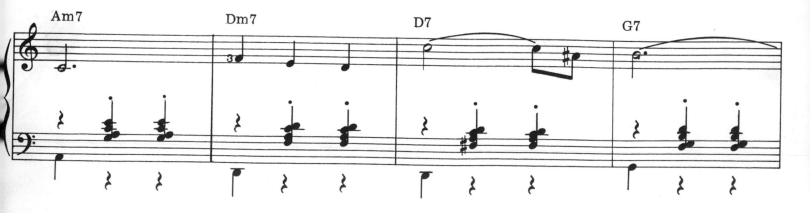

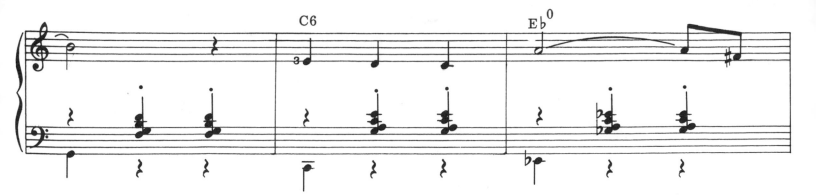

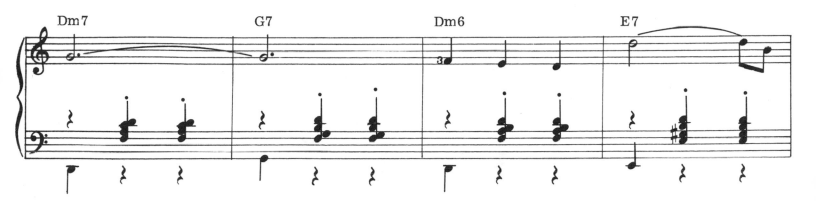

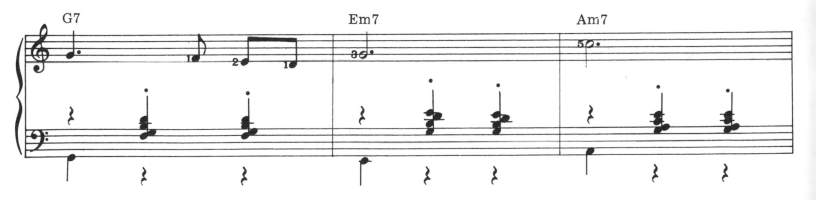

Basic Rhythm:- Chord:  (etc)
Pedal:

This is the same sort of idea as the Waltz (i.e. pedal followed by chord) but here we are in $\frac{4}{4}$ Time.

The above produces a rather more lively Foxtrot than the rhythm given earlier, but is harder to play. As in the Quick Waltz, the melody must be kept smooth whilst the left hand clips its chords short - a matter of nice coordination which may require considerable practice!

Registration No ①
Suggested Drum Rhythm:- Swing

Drifting And Dreaming

Words by Haven Gillespie.
Music by Egbert Van Alstyne,
Erwin R. Schmidt and Loyal Curtis

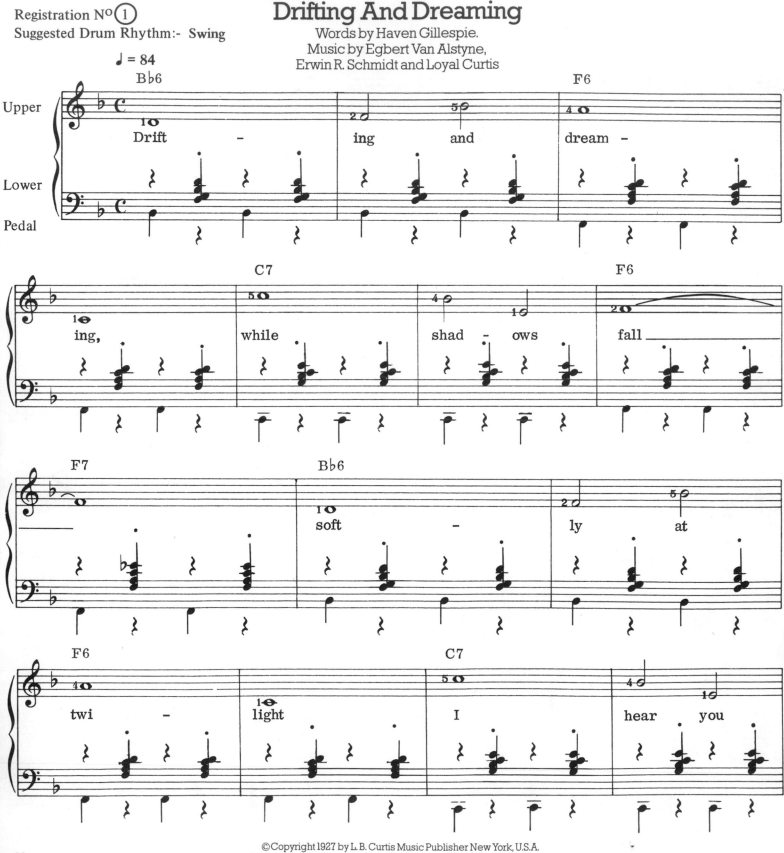

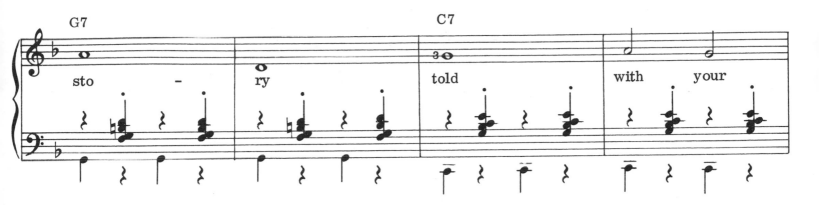

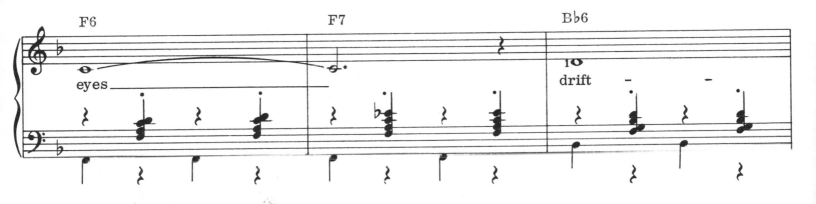

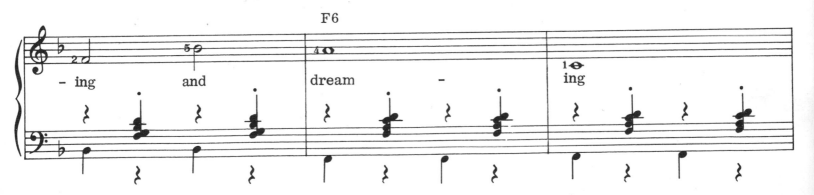

I'd Like To Teach The World To Sing

Words and Music by B. Backer, B. Davis, R. Cook and R. Greenaway

Registration Nº 1
Suggested Drum Rhythm:- Swing

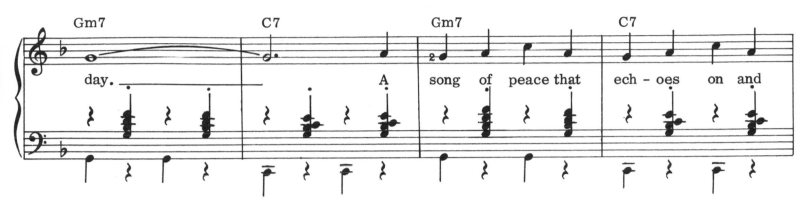

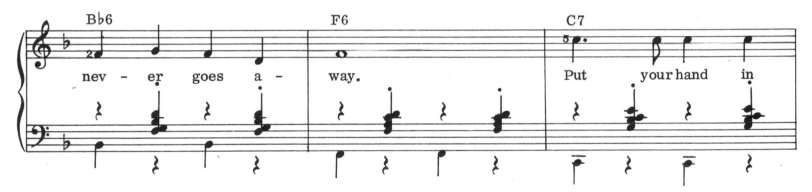

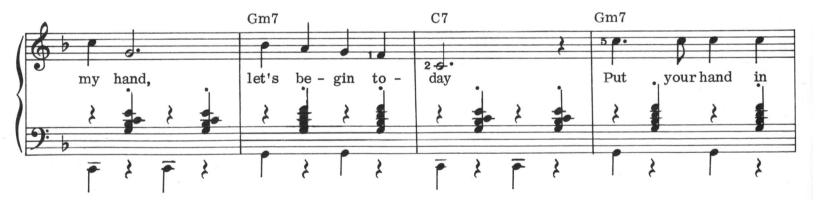

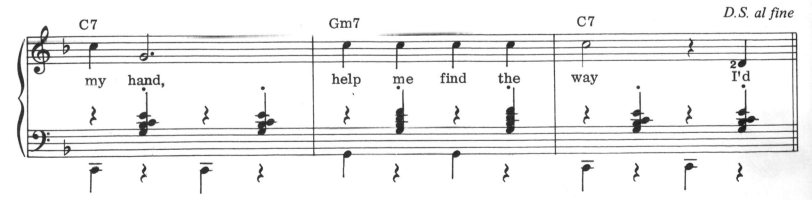

*ACCENT. A line like this over or under a note means hold that note for its full time
value. In other words, do NOT play it "Staccato"

23

A NEW DIMINISHED CHORD

This is the SECOND of our three basic DIMINISHED CHORDS:

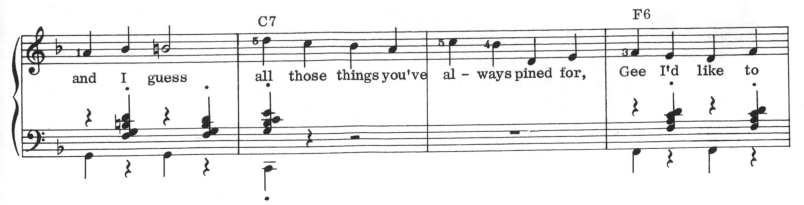

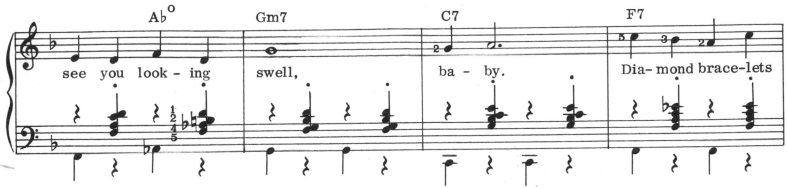

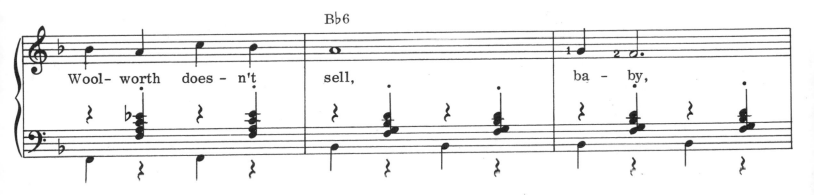

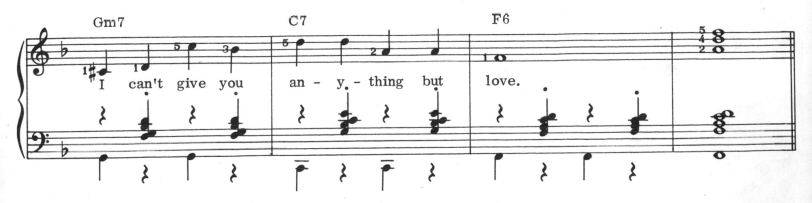

*i.e. Ab° with a B Pedal note.

This is the last of our three basic DIMINISHED CHORDS, and once again the rhythm of the piece is that of the QUICK WALTZ.

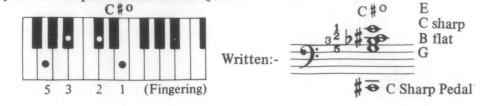

Whatever Will Be, Will Be (Que Sera, Sera)

Registration N⁰ ⑦

Words and Music by Jay Livingston and Ray Evans

Suggested Drum Rhythm:- Waltz

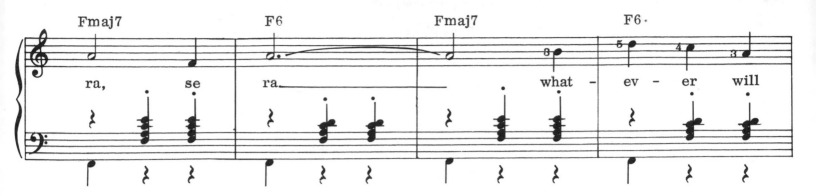

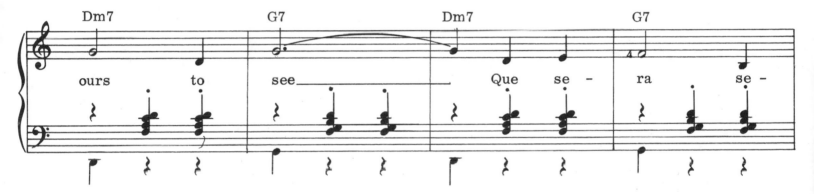

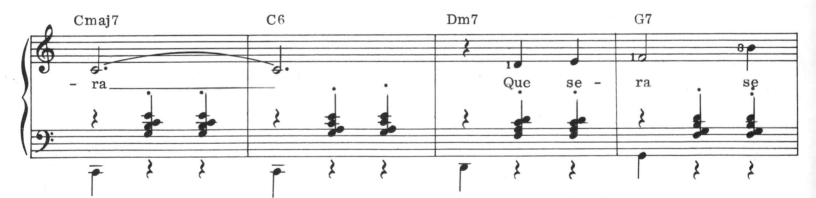

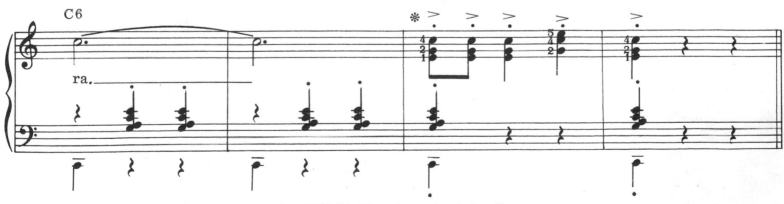

* ACCENT. Play these chords loudly.

Somewhere My Love

Words by Paul Francis Webster. Music by Maurice Jarre

Registration Nº ⑧
Suggested Rhythm:- Waltz

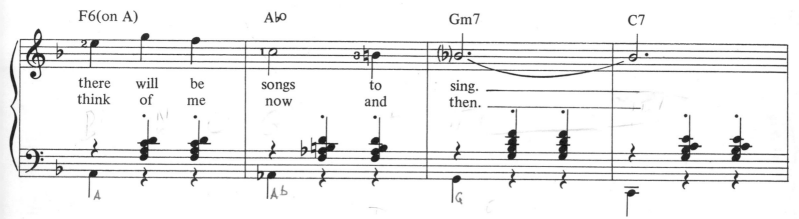

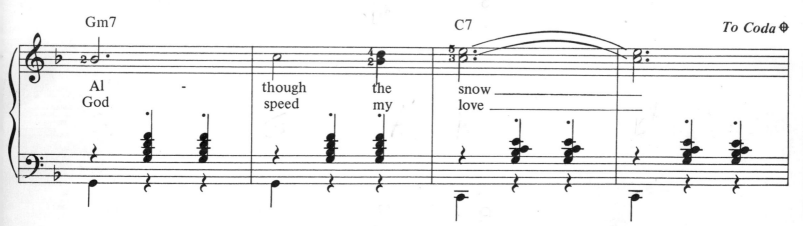

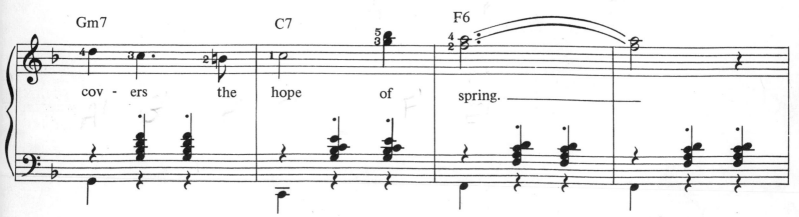

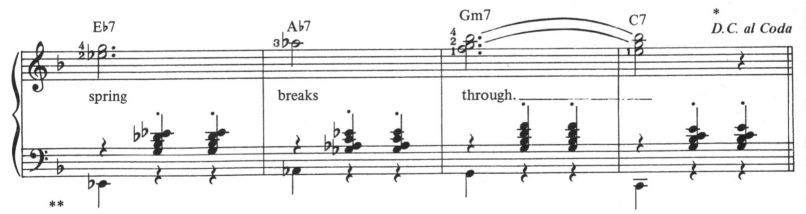

Da Capo al Coda: From the beginning to *CODA* (see REFERENCE, Dictionary of Musical Terms)
**CODA:* A final section (see REFERENCE, Dictionary of Musical Terms)

Side By Side

Words and Music by Harry Woods

Registration Nº 7
Suggested Drum Rhythm:- Swing

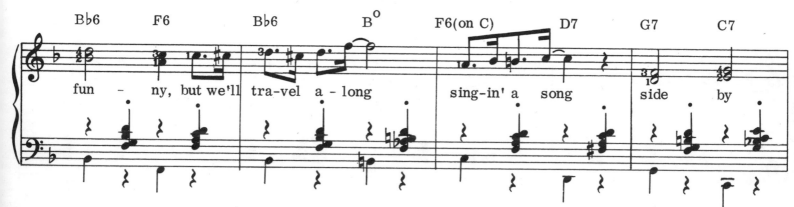

side by side. Thro' all kinds of wea-ther

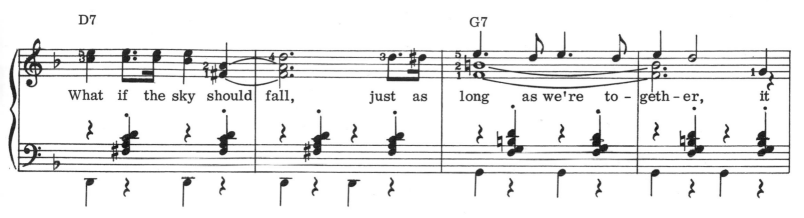

What if the sky should fall, just as long as we're to-geth-er, it

does-n't mat-ter at all When they've all had their quar-rels and

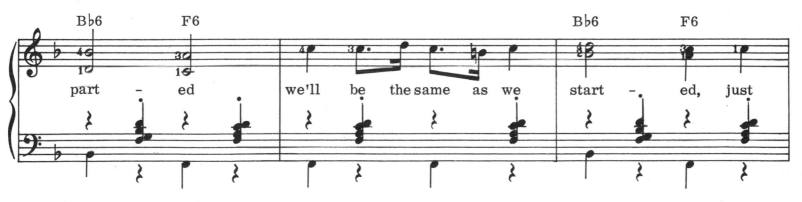

part - ed we'll be the same as we start - ed, just

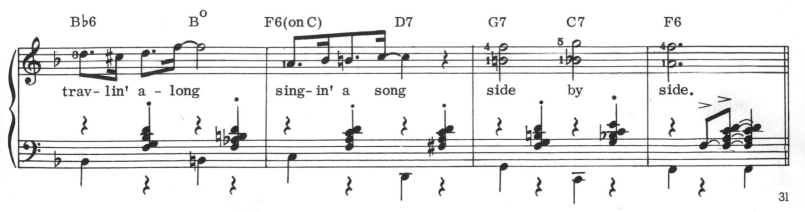

trav-lin' a - long sing-in' a song side by side.

The Entertainer
by Scott Joplin

Registration N°⑤
Suggested Drum Rhythm:- Swing *89/87*

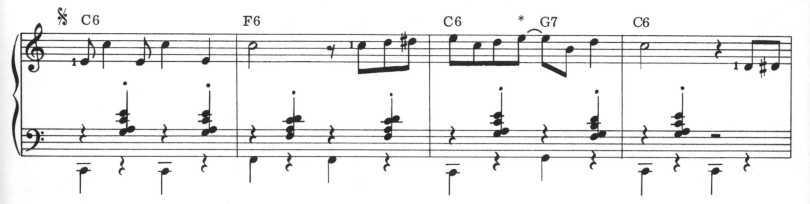

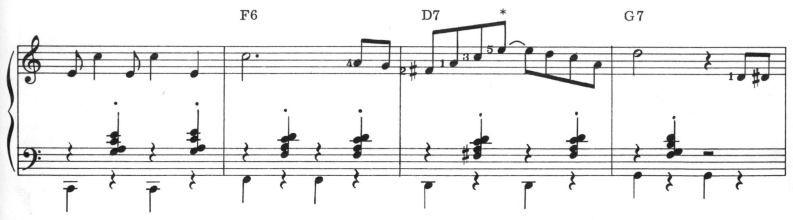

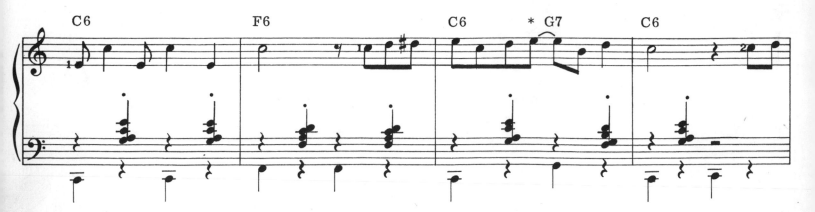

* Examples of "SYNCOPATION" (See Dictionary of Musical Terms (3))

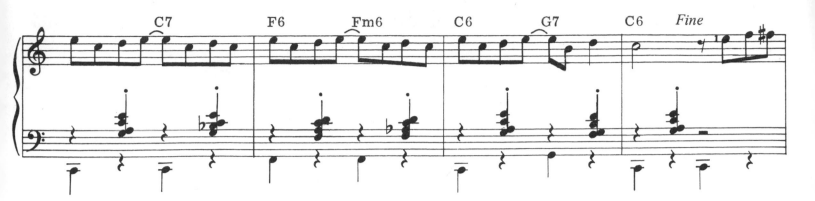

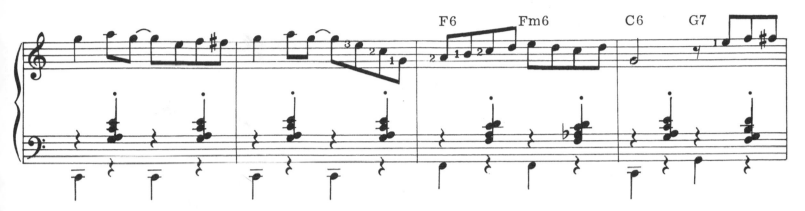

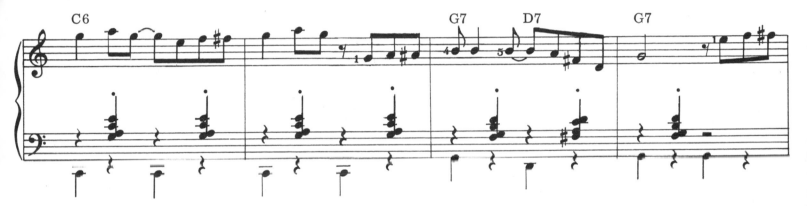

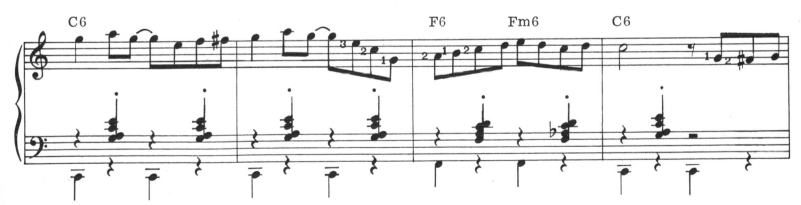

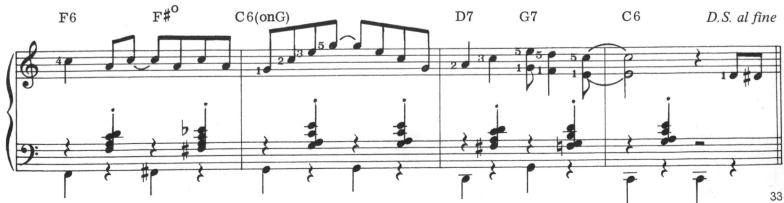

33

CHA-CHA-CHA

The second of our "Latin - American" rhythms. ("Bossa Nova" being the first)

Basic Rhythm: Chord:

Pedal:

(etc)

Count: 1   2 and 3   4 and

As in the Quick Waltz and Foxtrot(2) clip the left hand chords very short.

If you have no "Cha-Cha" rhythm available on your drum unit, use "Rock" (NOT "Slow Rock"). Failing that, some other Latin American rhythm such as "Bossa Nova" will do.

Swedish Rhapsody

Registration Nº ②
Suggested Drum Rhythm:- Cha Cha (or Rock)

Based on themes by Hugo Alfuen. Adaptation by Percy Faith

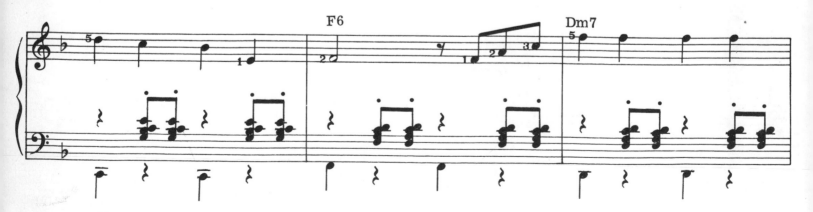

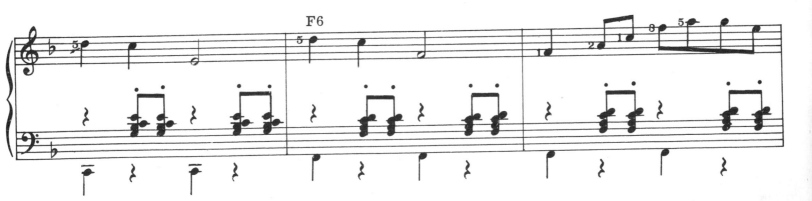

Patricia

By Perez Prado

Registration Nº ③
Suggested Drum Rhythm:- Cha Cha (or Rock)

To Coda ⊕

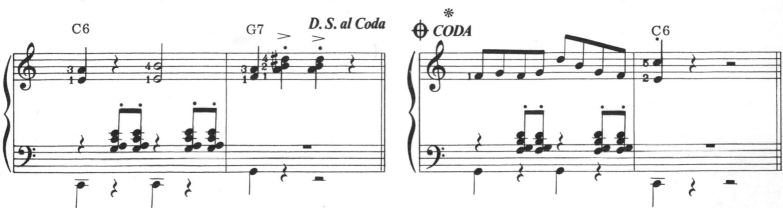

Never On Sunday

Words and Music by Billy Towne. Music by Manos Hadjidakis

Registration Nº ⑧
Suggested Drum Rhythm:- Cha Cha (or Rock)

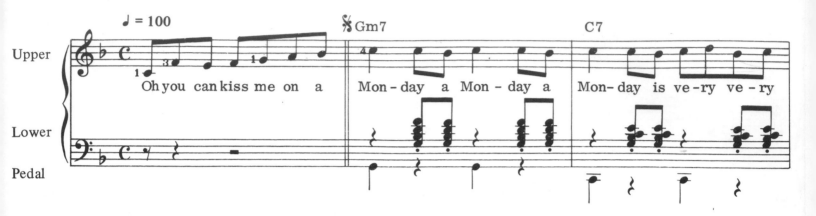

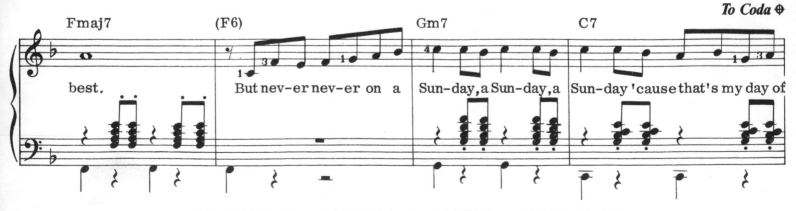

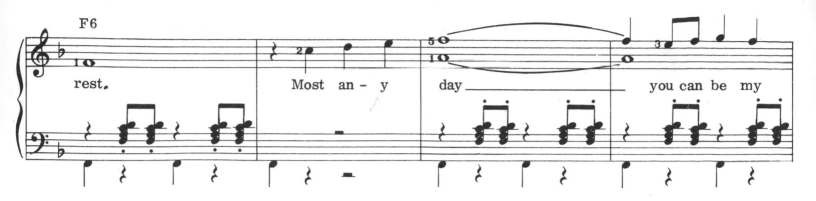

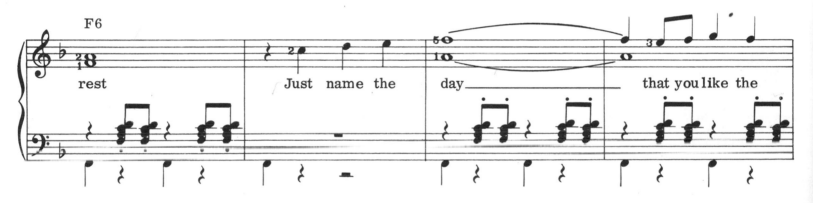

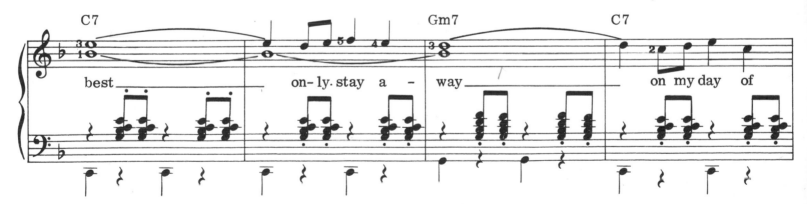

D. S. al Coda ✛ **CODA**

The note from which a chord takes its name is called the "Root". (The Root of C6 is "C"; the Root of Fm7 is "F"; the Root of B♭6 is "B♭", and so on).

Five Scale Notes above the Root lies another note used in the chord, called the "5th":-

These notes (The "Root" and the "5th") are the two most important notes of any chord for the pedals to play.

In the last two Cha-Chas in this book the pedals alternate between Roots and 5ths to good effect.

NOTE: Usually in an Alternating Bass Line the Root comes first followed by the 5th. Now and again, however, (as in the first two bars of "Sweet and Gentle") it is more effective and convenient to reverse the order, the 5th playing first.

Sweet And Gentle

Registration N⁰ ①
Suggested Drum Rhythm:- **Cha Cha (or Rock)**

Music by Otilio Portal. English lyric by George Thorn

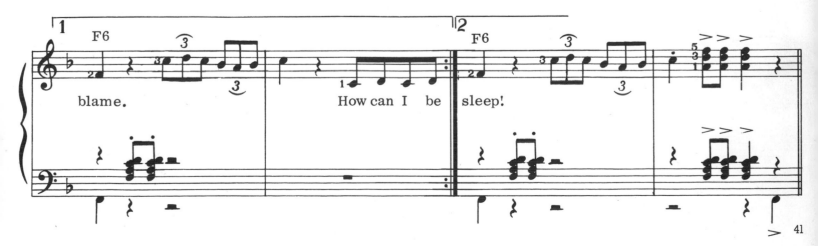

Something Stupid

Words and Music by C. Carson Parks

Registration Nº ⑥
Suggested Drum Rhythm:- Cha Cha (or Rock)

NEW MELODY NOTES

Written:-

B C

Middle C

B C

I know I stand in line un-til you think you have the time to spend an

eve-nin' with me_____ And if we go some place to dance I

know that there's a chance you won't be leav-in' with me_____ Then

af-ter-wards we drop in-to a qui-et lit-tle place and have a drink or two_____

REFERENCE SECTION
THE NOTES OF BOTH KEYBOARDS (MANUALS)
AND PEDAL-BOARD(S)

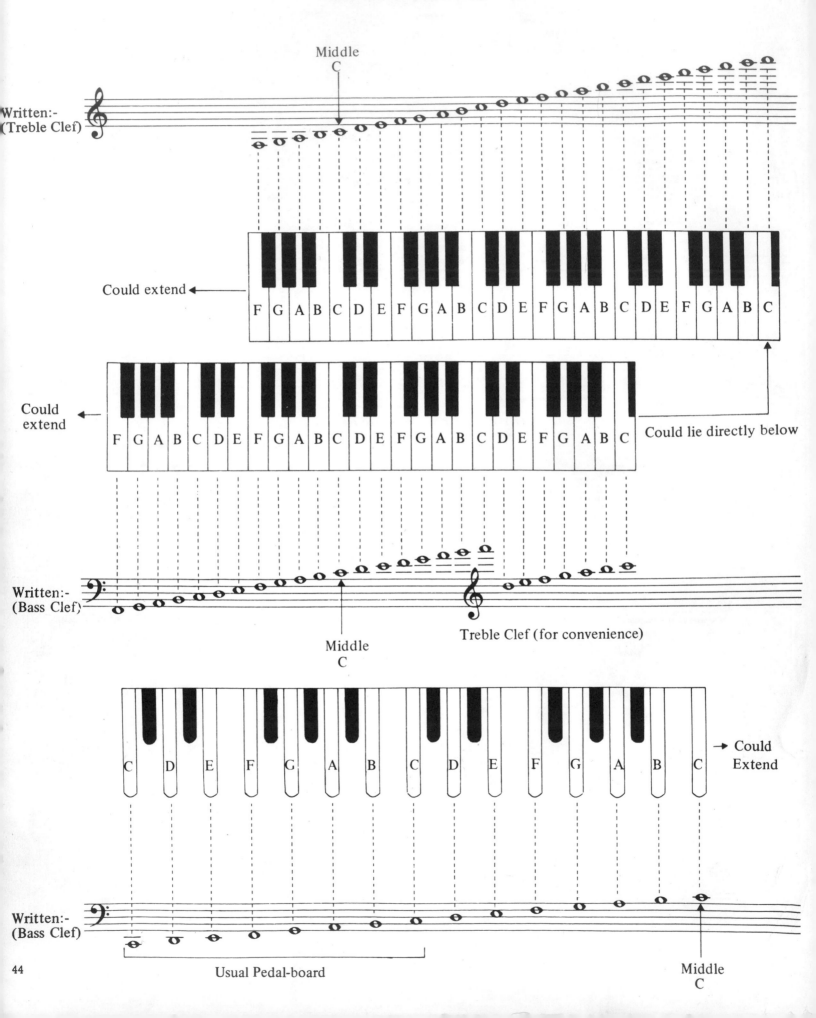

CHORD CHART (For Left Hand)
(Showing All Chords Used To Date)

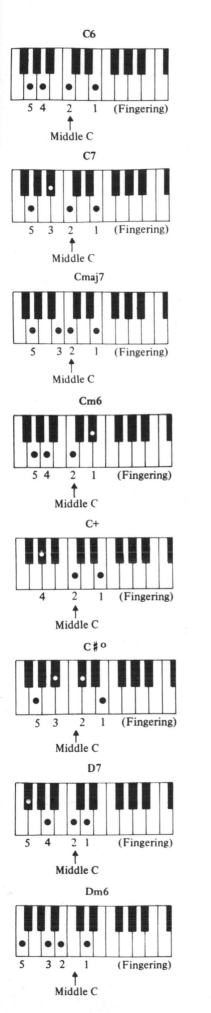

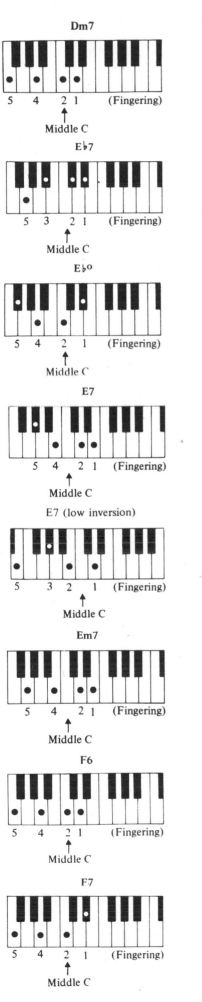

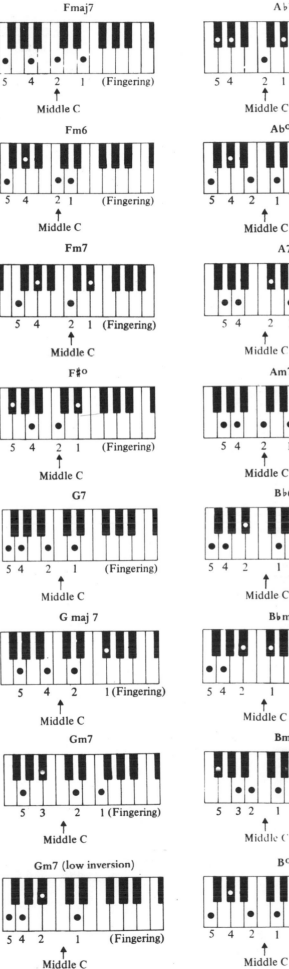

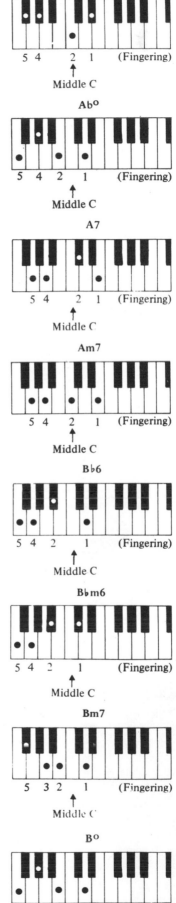

45

ACCENT ⟩ — Make the note (or notes) so marked prominent by playing it (or them) louder.

‒ — Make the note (or notes) so marked prominent by holding it (or them) for their full time value (or a little longer).

ACCIACCATURA ♪ — An ornament consisting of a discordant note struck together (or almost together) with that note immediately above. The Acciaccatura note is released at once, leaving the principal note singing.

AL FINE — "To the end". Usually used in conjunction with DA CAPO (D.C.) or DAL SEGNO (D.S.).

AUGMENTED CHORD (Written + or "aug") — A type of chord consisting of Root, 3rd (of the Major Scale), and 5th (of the Major Scale), the 5th being sharpened or "augmented" by one semitone.

BAION — A Latin-American dance rhythm.

BAION BASS | ♩. ♪♩ 𝄾 | played on the pedals.

CHA-CHA-CHA (CHA-CHA) — A Latin-American dance rhythm.

CODA (marked: ⊕) — A "tailpiece". A musical passage added to a piece in order to make a suitable ending. (See also DA CAPO and DAL SEGNO)

CROTCHET (QUARTER NOTE) TRIPLET — Three Crotchets (Quarter Notes) played in the time of two. Example:-

Crotchet Triplets

This sort of passage would probably best be counted in 2, like this:-

Count:-   1   tri – plet   2   1   and   2 – tri – plet
(say aloud)

The main beats (1,2,) must be kept perfectly regular whilst you play on and between them with the quicker notes.

DA CAPO (D.C.)	"From the beginning", i.e. repeat from the beginning of the piece. A useful device for saving space and the unnecessary turning of pages. It usually appears in one of the following two forms:—

    ①   "D.C. AL FINE", meaning: go back to the beginning of the piece and repeat from there until the word FINE is reached. There the piece ends.

    ②   "D.C. AL CODA", meaning: go back to the beginning of the piece and repeat from there until the small Coda sign is reached (marked ⊕ or *To Coda* ⊕). At that point jump ahead to the CODA (marked ⊕ *CODA*) and play to the end.

DAL SEGNO(D.S.)	"From the Sign" (𝄋). Another useful device for saving space and the unnecessary turning of pages. Examples:—

    ①   "D.S. AL FINE", meaning: go back to the Sign (𝄋) and repeat the passage from there until the word FINE is reached. There the piece ends.

    ②   "D.S. AL CODA" meaning: go back to the Sign (𝄋) and repeat the passage from there until the small Coda sign is reached (marked ⊕ or *To Coda* ⊕). At that point jump ahead to the CODA (marked ⊕ *CODA*) and play to the end.

DIMINISHED CHORD (Written ° or "dim")	Or "Diminished 7th" chord. A type of chord consisting of Root, 3rd (of the Major Scale) flattened by one semitone, and 5th (of the Major Scale) flattened by one semitone. To these three basic notes the "Diminished 7th" note may be added. The Diminished 7th note is the seventh note (of the Major Scale) flattened by TWO semitones.
FIFTH (5th)	The fifth note of a scale (counting the starting note of the scale as 1). One of the ingredients of a chord. An important Pedal (Bass Line) note.
MAJOR CHORD	A type of chord, consisting of Root, 3rd (of the Major Scale) and 5th (of the Major Scale).
MAJOR SCALE	The normal scale of adjoining notes used in present day music. (As opposed to Minor and other types of scale).
MINOR CHORD	A type of chord, consisting of Root, 3rd (of the Major Scale) flattened by one semitone, and 5th (of the Major Scale).

ROOT

The bottom note of a chord which has not been inverted. Forms the basis (i.e. starting note) of the scale from which the other chord notes are to be drawn. The most important pedal (Bass Line) note.

SEMITONE

The nearest possible distance on a keyboard (up or down).

SIGN (𝄋)

Used for the purpose of making a repeat.

SLUR

A curved line connecting two (different) notes. The second of the two notes is to be made less important than the first. On the organ this is usually done by making the second note staccato (detached).

SYNCOPATION

The displacement of one or more of the normal accented beats of a tune. Could be achieved by a note coming in just before a beat and being held (by means of a Tie) into the beat. Used quite extensively in Jazz and Pop Music.

THIRD (3rd)

The third note of a scale (counting the starting note of the scale as 1). One of the essential ingredients of a chord (being the only note differentiating between Major and Minor).